Everyone was in the playground.
Nadim had a surprise. It was a plastic
snake. He had bought it on holiday.

Mrs May called everyone inside.
Anneena had an idea. She wanted to
play a trick on Mrs May.

"Leave the snake here," she said.

The children went inside. Mrs May
told them to sit down.

"Mrs May! Mrs May!" called
Anneena. "I can see a snake in the
playground!"

"I can see it too!" said Wilf.

Everyone said they could see it. Mrs May looked outside.

"There *is* a snake outside," she said.

Mrs May gave Anneena a plastic bag.
She told her to put the snake in the bag.
"Oh, Mrs May, you knew it was a
plastic snake!" said Biff.

"Now for *my* snake," said Mrs May.
"What snake is that?" said Biff.
"The adder!" said Mrs May. "You can all do some addition sums!"

Everyone was doing addition sums.
The sums were hard. Then Wilf looked
outside.

"Look!" he yelled.

There was a donkey in the
playground.

"It's a donkey!" called Anneena.

"Mrs May! Mrs May!" everyone
called. "There's a donkey in the
playground!"

Mrs May looked cross.

"Is it made of plastic, too?" she said.

"It's true, Mrs May!" said Wilf. "Look out of the window!"

Mrs May looked out of the window.
She saw the donkey.

"Someone will have to catch it," said
Anneena.

"Mrs May can catch it with a plastic
bag!" called Nadim.
Mrs May was cross.
"Don't be silly, Nadim!" she said.

"Should we phone Animal Rescue?" asked Biff.

"That's a good idea, Biff," said Mrs May. "Sit quietly while I go to the phone."

At playtime the children talked about the donkey.

"It was easy to catch..." began Wilf.

"But then it wouldn't move," said Anneena.

"Two people pulled it…" began Chip.
"And two people pushed it!" said Biff.
"We didn't do any more work!" said
Nadim.

"Well, it's time to work now!" said
Mrs May. "Come back to the classroom.
You can learn to spell something."

"Spell what, Mrs May?" said Wilf.

"Donkey!" said Mrs May.
Everyone was doing spelling. Wilf looked
into the playground.
"Look!" he yelled.

There was a goose outside.

"It's a goose!" said Anneena. "Mrs
May! Mrs May! There's a goose in the
playground!"

Mrs May looked cross.

"Don't be silly, Anneena," she said.

"It's true, Mrs May!" said Chip.

"Look out of the window!"

Mrs May looked out of the window.
"Oh my goodness!" she said. "But it
may not be a goose. It may be a
gander."

"Will you call Animal Rescue?" said
Nadim.

"Yes," said Mrs May. "But I'm going
to shoo it on to the field. It can't stay in
the playground."

The children wanted to help.

"No," said Mrs May. "Sit quietly."
She went outside and waved her arms at
the gander.

The gander looked at Mrs May. Then it began to chase her.

"The gander has pecked Mrs May on the bottom!" yelled Biff.

Mrs May came inside.

"Are you all right, Mrs May?" asked Anneena.

"Yes, thank you," said Mrs May.

"I've got a joke," said Nadim. "What fruit do ganders like?"

"We don't know," said Chip.

"Gooseberries!" laughed Nadim.